Numbered details

My full name is ____.

In each of these details give the number in **figures**.

In my full name there are ________ letters.

I live at number ________. I am in Class ________.

Today's date is ________ ________ ________.
day month year

I am ________ years ________ months old.

I was born on ________ ________ ________.
day month year

In my class there are ________ boys and ________ girls, making ________ altogether.

Today there are ________ children absent.

________ children in my class have school meals today.

In an emergency, the teacher would dial ____________ on the telephone.

The school telephone number is ____________________.

I am ________ cm tall. I take size ________ shoes.

I usually have ________ pocket-money each week.

This is a car registration number which I know ____________________.

If a bus passes the school it has the Route Number ________ on it.

Some articles, including textbooks, have a registration or serial number on them.
I have found one in this room. It is ________________ on ________________.

In morning assembly, the hymn we sing most often is number ________.

I am on page ________ in my reading book. The book has ________ pages altogether.

Some people say they have lucky numbers.
In a competition, if I could pick three numbers between 0 and 100,
I would choose ________, ________ and ________.

Mixed pictures

To make a game, eight pictures were cut in half. The halves were then moved around, and this was the result.

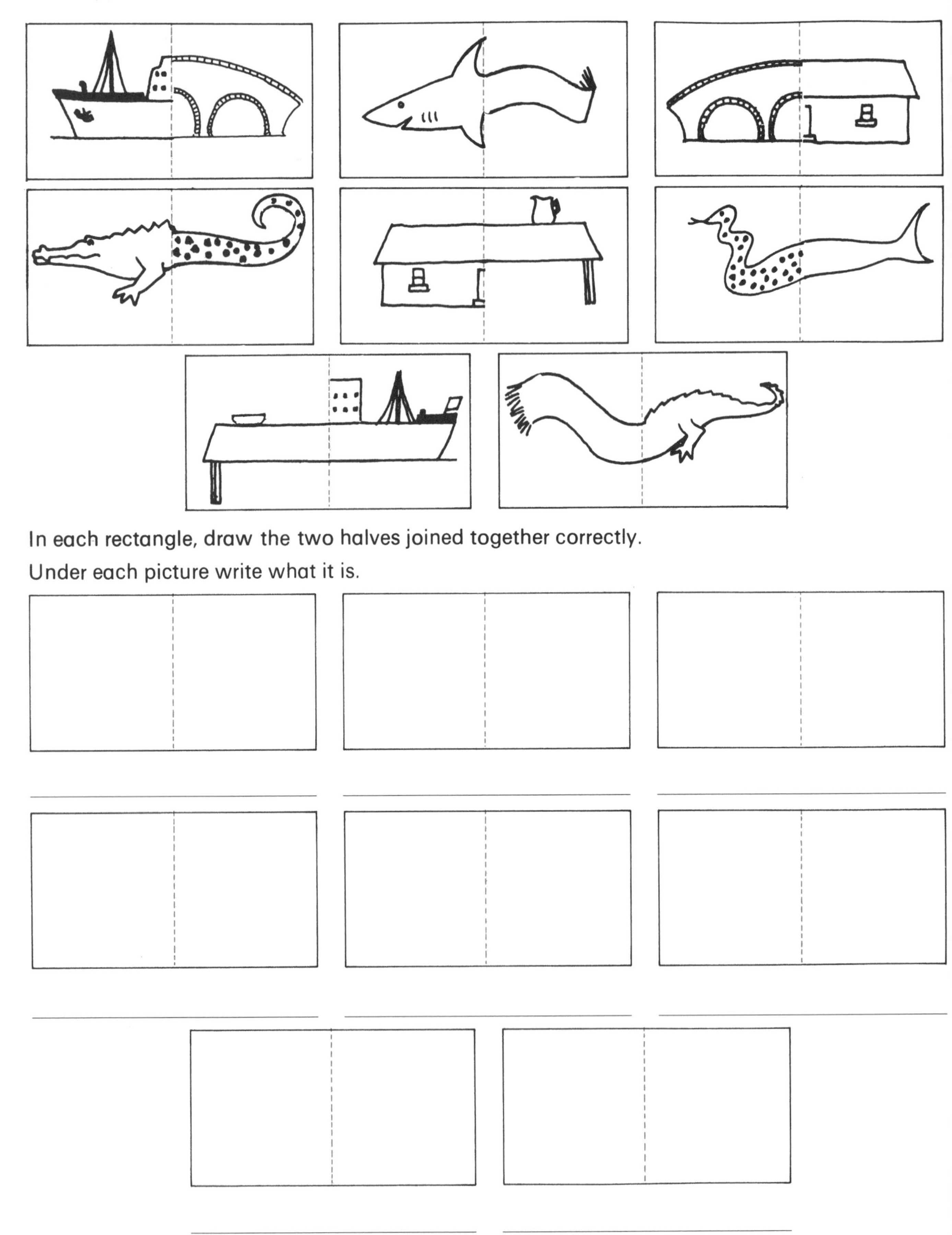

In each rectangle, draw the two halves joined together correctly.

Under each picture write what it is.

Words for pictures

Write a name for each picture. The word you write must **begin** or **end** with **ch**.

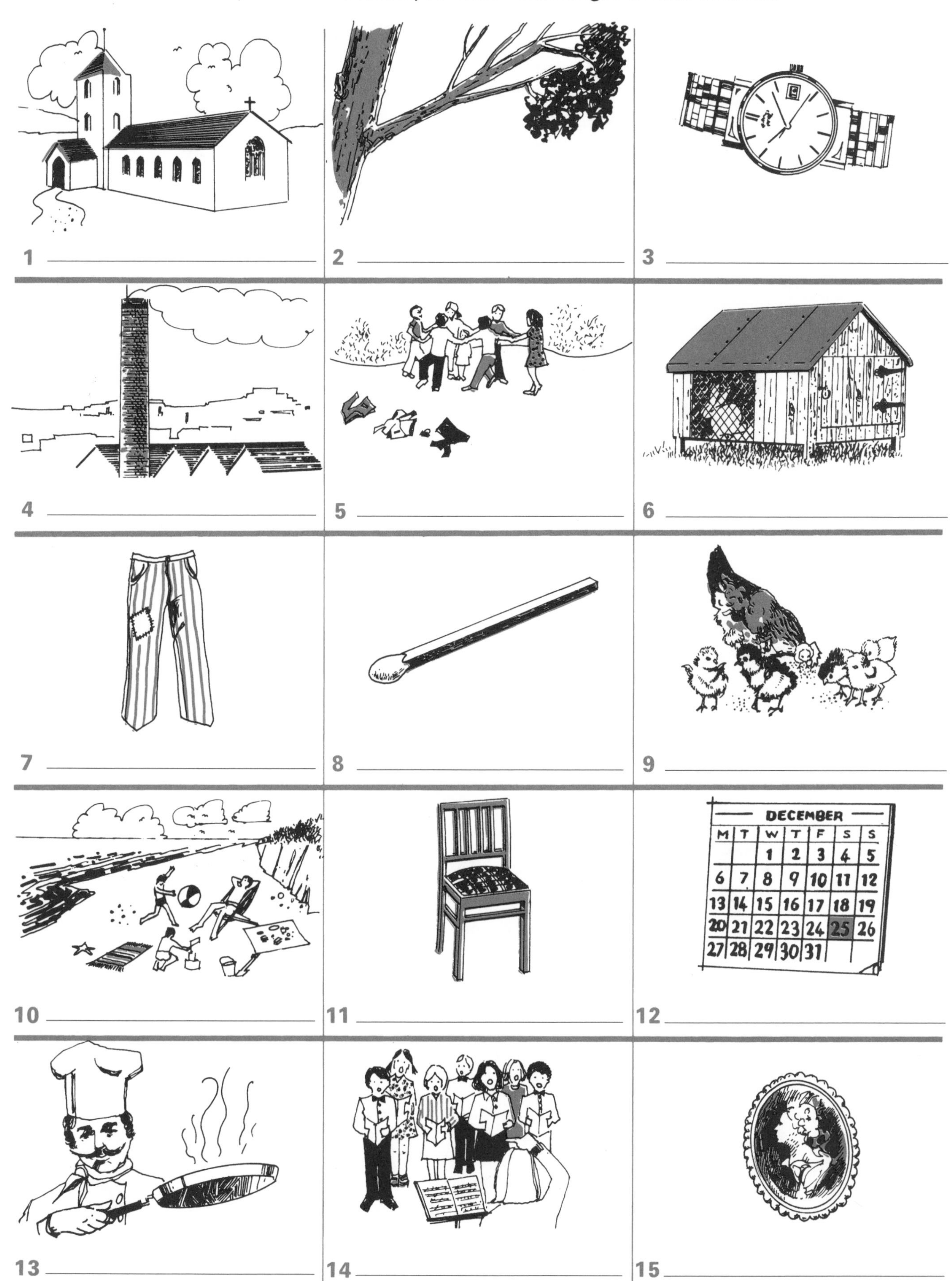

What are they doing?

From the two **verbs** in the panel, choose the correct one to write under each picture.

1
floating
swimming

2
pulling
pushing

3
laughing
crying

4
sleeping
resting

5
hopping
running

6
falling
climbing

7
chasing
running

8
reading
singing

9
striking
punching

10
conducting
directing

Adverbs

A verb is a 'doing' word. It describes an action.
An **adverb** tells you more about the **verb** or **action**.

For example, The sun shone **brightly**. (**brightly** is an adverb)
Please handle your fireworks **carefully**. (**carefully** is an adverb)
She nursed the baby **tenderly**. (**tenderly** is an adverb)

angrily	**cleverly**	**loudly**	**quietly**
bitterly	**gently**	**noisily**	**sadly**
calmly	**happily**	**peacefully**	**slowly**
cheerfully	**jerkily**	**quickly**	**strongly**

From this list, choose the best **adverbs** to add to each of the verbs on Page 4.

You may choose more than one adverb.

floating ______________________

swimming ______________________

pulling ______________________

pushing ______________________

laughing ______________________

crying ______________________

sleeping ______________________

resting ______________________

hopping ______________________

running ______________________

falling ______________________

climbing ______________________

chasing ______________________

reading ______________________

singing ______________________

striking ______________________

punching ______________________

conducting ______________________

directing ______________________

Adverbs—How would you do it?

carefully	**eagerly**	**proudly**	**sincerely**	**thoroughly**
clearly	**neatly**	**rapidly**	**swiftly**	**wearily**

From this list of adverbs, write the most suitable one to complete each answer to these questions. You must use each adverb once only.

1 How would you open a bird's cage?

I would open it ____________________ so that the bird would not fly out.

2 How do you wait for the postman on your birthday?

I wait for him ____________________, listening for his knock.

3 How do you wash your hands and face in the morning?

I am usually told to wash them ____________________.

4 How do you draw lines in your mathematics book?

I try to draw them ____________________, so that my shapes are correct.

5 How would you answer a call for help?

I would answer it ____________________.

6 If you won a medal, how would you show it to your family?

I would show it ____________________.

7 If you were asked to read a poem to the class, how would you do it?

I would read it ____________________, so that everyone could hear me.

8 How do you go to bed at night?

After being reminded it is time, I ____________________ climb the stairs.

9 What happens to your ice cream on a hot day?

It ____________________ disappears.

10 How do you end a letter you are writing to a friend?

I write, Yours ____________________ and then my name.

Groups

Ⓐ Write the name under each of the three pictures in the group.

Ⓑ Write the name of the group in column B. It may be more than one word.

Ⓒ Draw and name a fourth member of the group in column C.

Ⓑ	Ⓐ			Ⓒ
Group 1 These are all ______ ______.	______	______	______	______
Group 2 These are all ______ ______.	______	______	______	______
Group 3 These are all ______ ______.	______	______	______	______
Group 4 These are all ______ ______.	______	______	______	______
Group 5 These are all ______ ______.	______	______	______	______
Group 6 These are all ______ ______.	______	______	______	______
Group 7 These are all ______ ______.	______	______	______	______
Group 8 These are all ______ ______.	______	______	______	______

Similar—but different

Here are pairs of objects where, in each pair, the objects are similar in some way but different in another way.

Write the correct name under each picture.

Similar—but different

Complete two sentences about each pair of objects on page 8.

A Complete the first sentence by writing the correct word or phrase from this list.

buildings	**holes in the ground**
control electricity	**used for carrying**
footwear	**used for cutting**
kinds of weather	**used for sewing**
made from fruit and sugar	**worn on the nose**

B Complete the second sentence by copying the names of the objects from page 8.

1 Both are ______________________. A ______________ has two or more storeys, but a __________________ only has one.

2 Both are ______________________. ______________ falls as drops of water, but ______________ falls as frozen flakes.

3 Both are metal and are ______________________. A ______________ has a head, but a ______________ has an eye.

4 Both are ______________________. A ______________ is a hollow place in a rock, but a ______________ is made through rock by engineers.

5 Both are ______________. A ______________ covers the foot as high as the ankle, but the sole of a ______________ is held by straps.

6 Both are ______________________. ______________ have tinted lenses as a protection against strong light, but ______________ have clear lenses.

7 Both ______________________. A ______________ turns the current on or off, but a ______________ has to fit into a socket before the current will flow.

8 Both are ______________________. ______________ can be made from any kind of fruit, but ______________ is made only from citrus fruit, like oranges or lemons.

9 Both are ______________________. A ______________ is designed to carry school-books and is usually carried by a strap over the shoulder. You carry a ______________ by the handle, and it holds any of your belongings.

10 Both are ______________________. ______________ are larger than ______________.

About a bicycle

bell	carrier	dynamo	handlebars	mudguard	pump	stand
brake	chain	frame	lights	pedal	saddle	tyre

A From this list, write the correct name in each label.

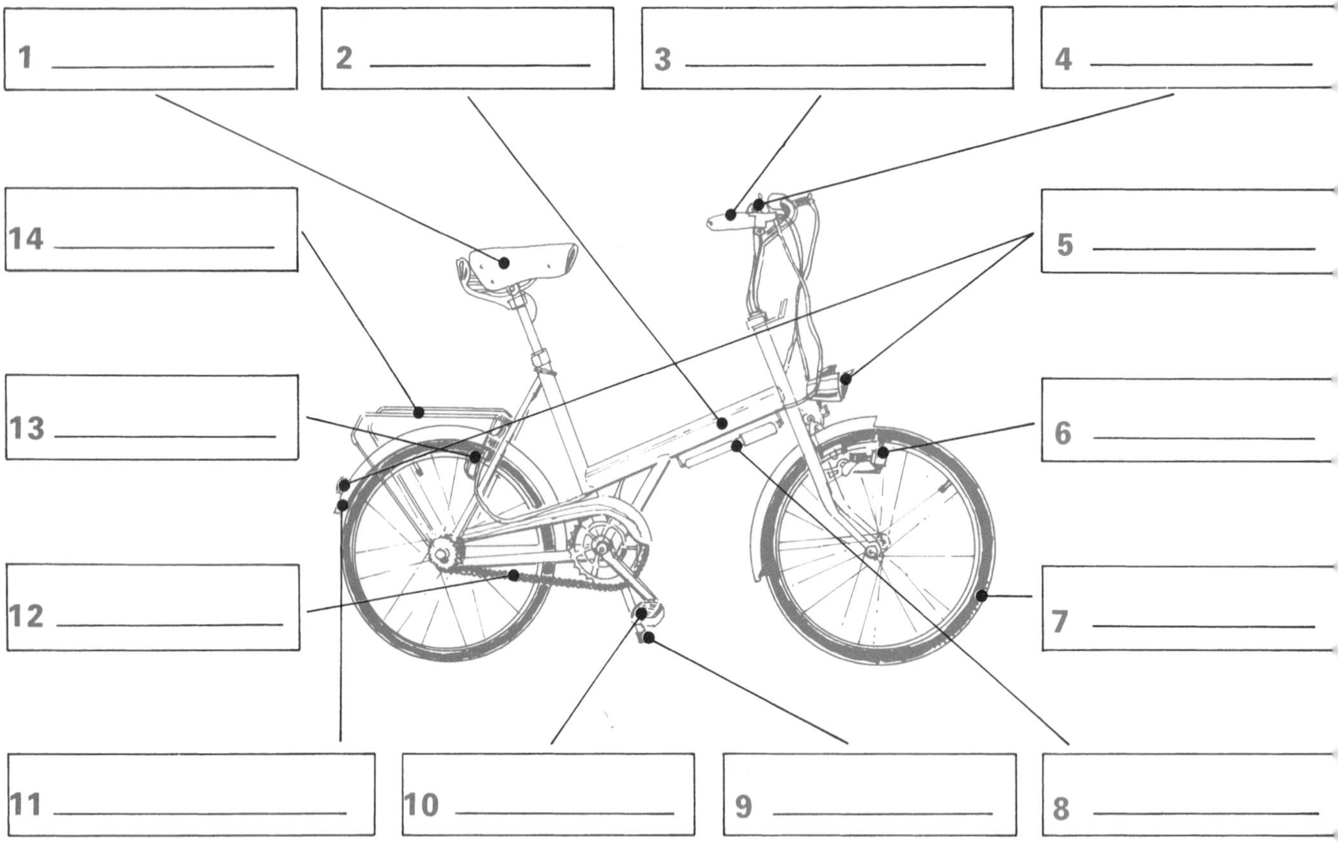

1 ______ 2 ______ 3 ______ 4 ______

14 ______ 5 ______

13 ______ 6 ______

12 ______ 7 ______

11 ______ 10 ______ 9 ______ 8 ______

B Write the correct name of the part in each of these hints.

1 Adjust the height of the ______ and the ______ to suit your height.

2 Check that the ______ is not too slack, or it will come off the gearwheel.

3 Check the pressure of each ______, and use the ______ if more air is neede

4 If it is likely to be dark, check that your front and rear ______ are working by engaging your ______ against the tyre wall.

5 When you are ready to start, kick the ______ into its clip, and make sure it is firmly fixed there.

6 Press each ______ with the ball of the foot.

7 Never apply the front ______ suddenly. It may throw you over the ______.

8 Never carry a bag or parcel in your hand. Fasten it securely to the ______.

9 Make a note of the registered number of your bicycle. You will find it stamped on the ______.

Group words

The four words in each of these groups have something in common.

Choose the correct word from the four to write under each picture.

Group 1
box
case
carton
packet

Group 2
gap
hole
leak
puncture

Group 3
length
piece
share
slice

Group 4
cable
rope
string
wire

Group 5
motorway
path
street
track

Group 6
bark
cover
peel
skin

Group 7
cut
fracture
graze
scratch

Group 8
fasten
fix
lock
tie

Places at the table

This drawing is a plan of the school meals table, showing where the children sit.

David

Ann Gill

Wayne Carol

Helen Elliot

Ben

A Answer these questions with the name of the child.

1 Who is **between** Ann and Gill? ____________

2 Who is sitting on the **left** of Ben? ____________

3 Who is **opposite** Ann? ____________

4 Who is **opposite** Helen? ____________

5 Who is **between** Elliot and Gill? ____________

6 Who is sitting on the **right** of Helen? ____________

7 Who has Ann on the **left** and Helen on the **right**? ____________

8 The teacher made a rule that a boy must sit with a girl on his **left**, and a girl on his **right**. Which two children must change places to keep to this rule?

____________ and ____________

9 The children take turns to be 'server' in alphabetical order.

Today David is 'server'. Who will it be tomorrow? ____________

In five days' time whose turn will it be? ____________

10 Think, for a moment, of the name of a sea-creature with eight arms.
Now, **underline** the correct name of the shape of the table.

triangle	**pentagon**	**septilateral**	**octagon**
square	**hexagon**	**nonagon**	**decagon**

B In this space draw a plan of the table at which you usually have your meals. Write the names of the people in their places at the table.

C Using the words in Section A, describe the position of each person.

____
____
____
____
____
____
____
____

Engagements

To remind them of what is to happen, people often write down engagements in a diary.

A Write the time, **in words**, under the figures for each of these engagements:

actress	caretaker	footballer	policeman	reporter
air hostess	chef	kennel-maid	postman	teacher

B From this list, write in column B, the name of the person who wrote down the engagement.

A		B
10.30 a.m.		
______________	point duty—city centre	______________
8.00 a.m.		
______________	exercise and feed terriers	______________
12.00 p.m.		
______________	flight 607 to Singapore	______________
4.30 p.m.		
______________	empty Lea Road pillar-box	______________
3.30 p.m.		
______________	prepare menu for dinner	______________
6.30 p.m.		
______________	jumble sale at school	______________
9.45 a.m.		
______________	report for start of new play	______________
10.00 a.m.		
______________	first-team training session	______________
7.30 a.m.		
______________	engineer coming to check boiler	______________
11.15 a.m.		
______________	interview M.P. at his office	______________

C Make a note here of three of **your** engagements during the coming week.
Give the **date**, the **time** and **what is to happen**.

1 ______________________________.

2 ______________________________.

3 ______________________________.

Verbs — Present and Past

The **verb** in a sentence tells you when an action takes place.

For example,

Today I **am** in good time for school. (The verb is **in the present**.)

Yesterday I **was** late for school. (The verb is **in the past**.)

I **think** I **have** a cold. (The verbs are **in the present**.)

Before I **left**, Mum **thought** I **had** something wrong with me. (The verbs are **in the past**.)

Fill in the spaces in these sentences by writing the underlined verbs **in the past**.

1 This is the day when I **swim** a length. Last week I ____________ two widths.

2 Each day I **walk** over one kilometre. Once I ____________ over ten kilometres.

3 Tonight I **go** to the dancing class. Last night I ____________ to the cinema.

4 I **am writing** to my friend Susan. She ____________ to me last month.

5 We **are singing** some carols today. We ____________ them last Christmas.

6 There **are** five eggs in the nest. Yesterday there ____________ only four.

7 I **am making** a new clay pot. I ____________ a mess of the first one.

8 It **is** fine and we **can** go on to the field. When it ____________ wet we ____________ not go out.

9 I know someone who **is running** in the Olympics. He ____________ for the county team last year.

10 This term we **are eating** our meals in the new dining-hall. Last term we ____________ them in the large class-room.

11 My dad **sells** cars. Yesterday he ____________ a new Rover.

12 Today the passengers **fly** to New York. Yesterday they ____________ into Heathrow.

13 I **find** this page difficult. I ____________ page 13 rather easy.

14 The jockey **rides** at Ascot today. Yesterday he ____________ at Newcastle.

15 My sister usually **does** her homework after tea. Last Saturday she ____________ some in the morning.

16 I expect Leeds to **win** today. They ____________ against the same team last season.

17 Please **give** generously. Last year you ____________ over fifty pounds.

18 The team **meets** at the village inn. It last ____________ there in October.

19 She **comes** to see us once a week. Last week she ____________ on Thursday.

20 I **take** my cycling test today. It is two years since my brother ____________ the same test and passed.

Verbs in the P.E. lesson

These pictures show actions which take place during the P.E. lesson.

bounce	catch	climb	jump	pull	run	stretch	throw
carry	chase	hit	lie	roll	sit	swing	walk

A From these verbs:
write the verb **in the present**, as though it is happening **now**. Use each one once only.

1 Wayne is ______________ up the bars.
2 Kim is ______________ over a cane.
3 Larry is ______________ after a hoop.
4 Paul is ______________ up the mat.
5 Sue is ______________ the trolley.
6 Ann is ______________ with a ring on her head.
7 David is ______________ on the rope.
8 Ian is ______________ his arms and legs.
9 Wendy is ______________ a ball.
10 Dan is ______________ some hoops.
11 Carol is ______________ a ball.
12 Tim is ______________ a ball.
13 Lucy is ______________ on a bench.
14 Gary is ______________ on a mat.
15 John is ______________ a ball.
16 Helen is ______________ her friend.

B Write the verb **in the past**, as though it happened **yesterday**.

1 Wayne ______________ up the bars.
2 Kim ______________ over a cane.
3 Larry ______________ after a hoop.
4 Paul ______________ up the mat.
5 Sue ______________ the trolley.
6 Ann ______________ with a ring on her head.
7 David ______________ on the rope.
8 Ian ______________ his arms and legs.
9 Wendy ______________ a ball.
10 Dan ______________ some hoops.
11 Carol ______________ a ball.
12 Tim ______________ a ball.
13 Lucy ______________ on a bench.
14 Gary ______________ on a mat.
15 John ______________ a ball.
16 Helen ______________ her friend.

Give or take a letter

A word within a word

A By **taking** a letter from a word, you may still have another word.

For example,

hate	take away	**e**	makes	**hat**
buoy	take away	**u**	makes	**boy**
buoy	take away	**o**	makes	**buy**
twig	take away	**t**	makes	**wig**

Take a letter from each of these words to make another word.

word	take away	makes	word	take away	makes	word	take away	makes
1 across	__	________	11 cheat	__	________	21 hoard	__	________
2 angler	__	________	12 china	__	________	22 hoot	__	________
3 asleep	__	________	13 crush	__	________	23 know	__	________
4 badger	__	________	14 drain	__	________	24 moist	__	________
5 barge	__	________	15 east	__	________	25 patch	__	________
6 blast	__	________	16 eyes	__	________	26 plaice	__	________
7 bread	__	________	17 float	__	________	27 psalm	__	________
8 camel	__	________	18 gown	__	________	28 rouse	__	________
9 care	__	________	19 hair	__	________	29 scent	__	________
10 cease	__	________	20 halt	__	________	30 weave	__	________

B By **adding** a letter to a word, you can sometimes make another word.

For example,

each	add	**b**	makes	**beach**
pace	add	**e**	makes	**peace**
shot	add	**o**	makes	**shoot**

Add a letter to each of these words to make another word.

word	add	makes	word	add	makes	word	add	makes
1 ever	__	________	11 pant	__	________	21 rough	__	________
2 oil	__	________	12 pie	__	________	22 tread	__	________
3 fair	__	________	13 ice	__	________	23 towel	__	________
4 father	__	________	14 sale	__	________	24 win	__	________
5 rain	__	________	15 sore	__	________	25 word	__	________
6 night	__	________	16 cream	__	________	26 even	__	________
7 law	__	________	17 nail	__	________	27 pure	__	________
8 lose	__	________	18 son	__	________	28 scar	__	________
9 moth	__	________	19 stag	__	________	29 tart	__	________
10 nose	__	________	20 star	__	________	30 wait	__	________

Sentences in order

 These pictures show the **life story of a butterfly** in the correct order.

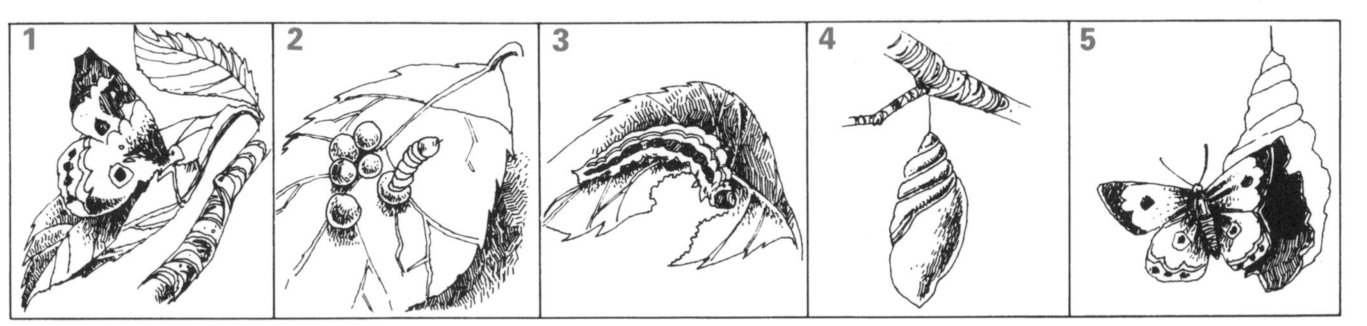

These sentences describe the five stages in the life of a butterfly, but they are in the **wrong order**.

It then hangs by its tail from a silken thread to become a chrysalis with a hard skin.

The larva breaks out of the egg.

After three weeks, the skin breaks and out comes a butterfly with damp wings.

It feeds hungrily on the leaves of the host plant.

The butterfly lays its eggs in a cluster on the leaf.

Write out the sentences in their **correct order**.

1 ______________________________.

2 ______________________________.

3 ______________________________.

4 ______________________________
______________________________.

5 ______________________________
______________________________.

B  These sentences describe five stages in the making of **bricks,** but they are in the **wrong order**.

A long band of this clean clay is forced through a hole.

Finally, the bricks are 'fired' in a kiln and are stacked ready for use.

It is dug up by excavators and cleaned.

As it comes through the hole, it is cut to shape and size by wires.

Clay for bricks is found on the beds of dried-up lakes or rivers.

Write out the sentences in their **correct order**.

1 ______________________________.

2 ______________________________.

3 ______________________________.

4 ______________________________.

5 ______________________________
______________________________.

Spelling — How does it end?

Although the **endings** of many words may sound nearly the same, they may be spelt differently.
For example, stamin**a** cell**ar** ang**er** err**or** hum**our** mit**re** leis**ure**

a	ar	er	or	our	re	ure

From these seven different endings, write the correct **ending** to complete each of these words.
(In each group no two endings are spelt the same.)

- ac ________
- act ________
- add ________
- alt ________
- are ________

- bachel ________
- badg ________
- banan ________

- caterpill ________
- camer ________
- cent ________
- chapt ________
- col ________
- conduct ________

- dang ________
- doct ________
- doll ________

- equat ________

- fath ________
- fib ________
- fig ________
- flav ________

- gramm ________
- glam ________

- hamm ________
- hang ________
- hon ________

- ide ________

- jagu ________
- join ________

- knock ________

- lab ________
- ladd ________
- larv ________
- lect ________
- liqu ________
- lit ________
- lun ________

- mani ________
- matt ________
- met ________
- mirr ________
- moist ________
- mort ________

- nat ________
- nect ________
- numb ________

- Octob ________
- orchestr ________

- pap ________
- perambulat ________
- popul ________
- press ________
- pum ________

- quart ________
- quot ________

- rapt ________
- raz ________
- record ________
- regul ________
- rumb ________
- rum ________

- sab ________
- sail ________
- sauc ________
- savi ________
- script ________
- sultan ________

- tail ________
- tart ________
- teach ________
- tombol ________
- treas ________

- upp ________

- vanill ________
- verg ________
- vig ________
- vineg ________
- visit ________
- vult ________

- wait ________
- warri ________

- youngst ________

- zebr ________
- zith ________

Finding your way

This is part of a town plan showing some of the important buildings and features.

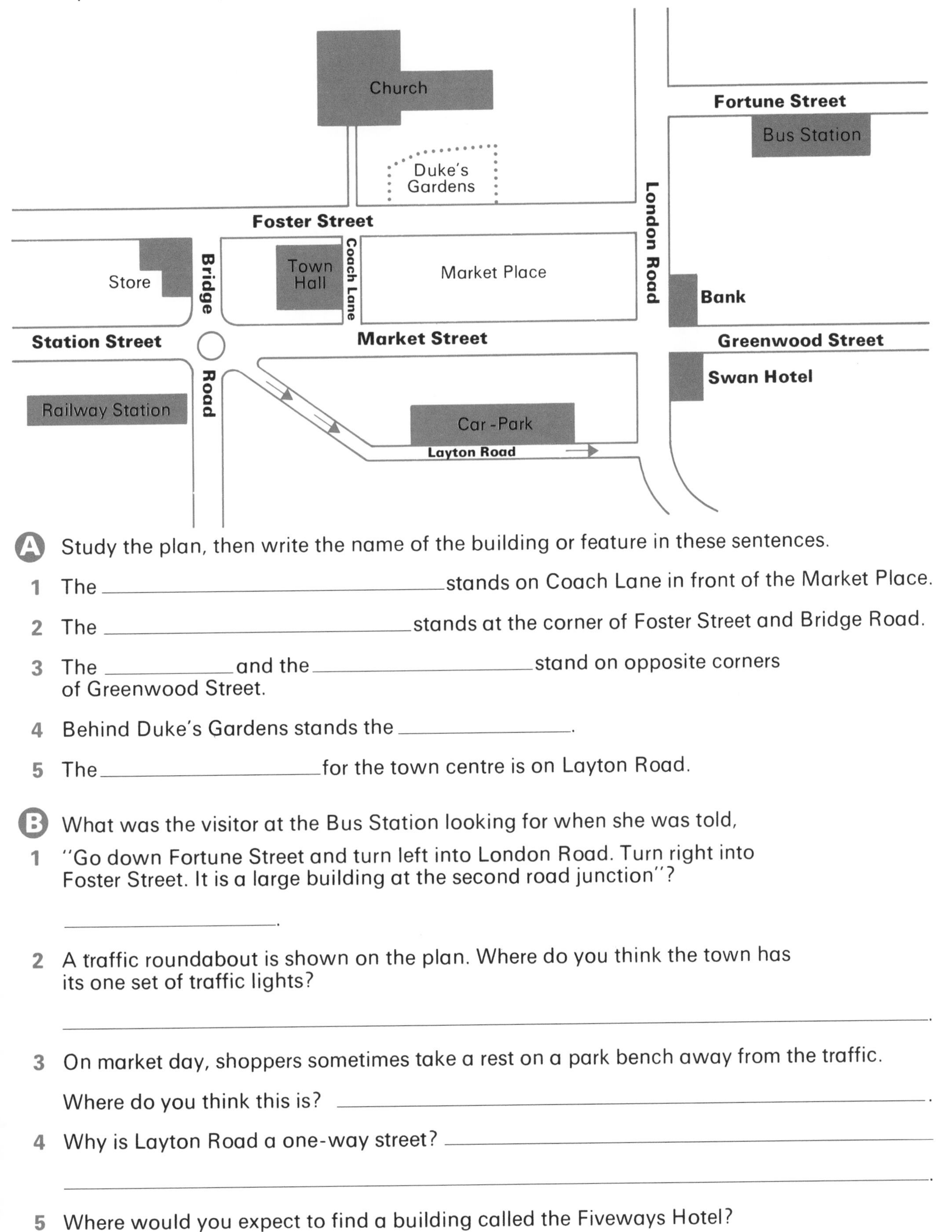

A Study the plan, then write the name of the building or feature in these sentences.

1. The ____________________ stands on Coach Lane in front of the Market Place.
2. The ____________________ stands at the corner of Foster Street and Bridge Road.
3. The ____________ and the ____________________ stand on opposite corners of Greenwood Street.
4. Behind Duke's Gardens stands the ____________________.
5. The ____________________ for the town centre is on Layton Road.

B What was the visitor at the Bus Station looking for when she was told,

1. "Go down Fortune Street and turn left into London Road. Turn right into Foster Street. It is a large building at the second road junction"?

   ____________________.

2. A traffic roundabout is shown on the plan. Where do you think the town has its one set of traffic lights?

   ____.

3. On market day, shoppers sometimes take a rest on a park bench away from the traffic.

   Where do you think this is? ____________________________________.

4. Why is Layton Road a one-way street? ____________________________________

   ____.

5. Where would you expect to find a building called the Fiveways Hotel?

   ____.

Word meanings

For each word three meanings are given. Only one of these meanings is correct.
Choose the correct meaning and write it in a sentence.

an ambush
- a bush on which almonds grow
- a surprise attack
- a band worn on the arm

1 An ambush is ________________.

a combat
- a long cricket bat
- an African flying-mouse
- a fight

2 A combat is ________________.

a drought
- continuous dry weather
- a current of air
- a game for two with counters

3 A drought is ________________

________________.

an excursion
- a pardon
- a pleasure-trip
- a shutting-out

4 An excursion is ________________.

flour
- a storey of a building
- a blossom
- finely-ground wheat

5 Flour is ________________

________________.

a goblin
- a mischievous fairy
- a drinking vessel
- a tool for boring holes

6 A goblin is ________________.

a route
- the way or road to travel
- part of the plant underground
- a wheel track or furrow

7 A route is ________________.

a scar
- a fright
- something difficult to obtain
- a mark left by a wound

8 A scar is ________________.

seize
- to see clearly
- to grip or capture
- lakes or oceans

9 Seize means ________________

a site
- something seen
- a long bench or couch
- ground on which a building stands

10 A site is ________________

____

miser
- one who is mean with his money
- the spelling of Mr.
- one who breeds white mice

11 A miser is ________________

____

a kingfisher
- a small brightly-coloured diving-bird
- a champion angler
- the chief of a tribe

12 A kingfisher is ________________

____

a tenor
- a ten-pound note (slang)
- a male singer of high notes
- one who rents a house

13 A tenor is ________________.

a signal
- one on its own
- a kind of finger ring
- a message given by signs

14 A signal is ________________.

a noose
- a loop with a running knot
- a man from the north
- a giant American deer

15 A noose is ________________.

Word meanings and spellings

One out of three

In each of these sentences, out of the three words in the brackets **underline** the one which is correct for meaning and spelling.

1 I had not carried the heavy parcel long before my arms began to (ace, ache, hake).

2 If you bring me some flour from the shop, I can (back, bake, beak) some bread.

3 The (bark, brake, break) on his bicycle needs repairing.

4 May I please (barrow, borrow, burrow) your felt pen?

5 There was a loud (chair, char, cheer) from the crowd as the team came out.

6 We have a (daily, dally, dale) delivery of milk.

7 My (dreary, dairy, diary) gives the times of sunrise and sunset.

8 When I was not looking, John (eight, ate, eat) my piece of cake.

9 You ought to have a ticket to show that you have paid your (fair, fare, fear).

10 We have a special (guessed, guest, guise) for dinner today.

11 The prince is the (hare, hair, heir) to the throne.

12 The factory is closed and the machines stand (idle, idol, idyll).

13 Another egg has been (lade, laid, laird) in the nest.

14 The postman was late in delivering the (male, meal, mail) today.

15 We have a secret hide-out where we (meat, meet, mete) every Saturday.

16 A (nave, navy, navvy) is a labourer.

17 The first prize in the draw has been (one, own, won) by ticket number seven.

18 When I was a bridesmaid, I carried a (pose, poser, posy) of flowers.

19 This is the (receipt, recipe, recite) for the money you paid last week.

20 It does not (same, seam, seem) four weeks since we broke up for a holiday.

21 There is a weather-vane on the (spare, spear, spire) of the church.

22 Did you know that you have a flat (tire, trier, tyre)?

23 It took me a long time to get the cotton (though, thorough, through) the eye of the needle.

24 The bag of sugar should (way, weigh, whey) one kilogram.

25 Try this belt around your (waste, whist, waist).

Why?

Give a clear answer, in sentences, to each of these questions.

Add as much interesting information as you can.

1 Why does a football boot have studs?

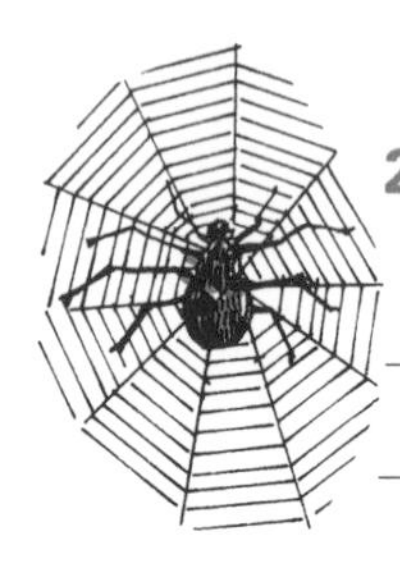

2 Why does a spider spin its web?

3 Why does this coin have a milled edge?

4 Why does a duck have webbed feet?

5 Why does a chimney have lead flashing ?

6 Why does an orange have pips?

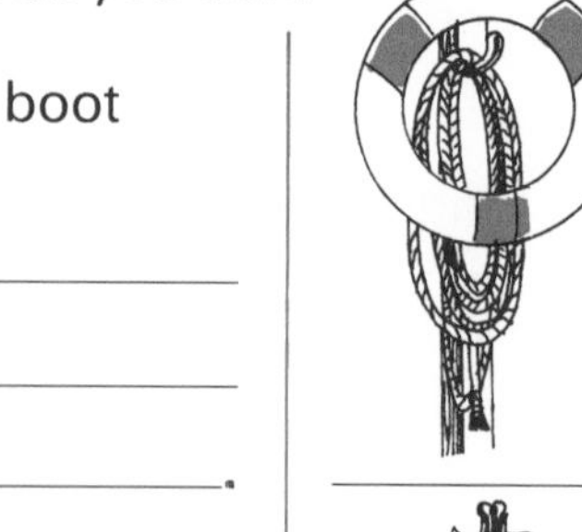

7 Why does a lifebelt have a rope attached?

8 Why does a giraffe have such a long neck?

9 Why does a railway truck have buffers?

10 Why does a postage stamp have a perforated edge?

11 Why are the three insulated wires of an electric cable in different colours?

12 Why does a plant pot have a hole at the bottom?

The two sexes — Masculine and Feminine

Some words are **masculine** and tell you that a person or creature is **male**.

For example, boy, king, bull are masculine words.

Other words are **feminine** and tell you that a person or creature is **female**.

For example, girl, queen, cow are feminine words.

In each of these groups, write in the missing masculine or feminine words.

Group 1 People in the family

Masculine	**Feminine**
father	______
son	______
______	sister
______	niece
uncle	______

Group 2 People with titles

Masculine	**Feminine**
king	______
______	princess
______	duchess
knight or lord	______
______	baroness
mayor	______

Group 3 Other people

Masculine	**Feminine**
actor	______
______	comedienne
man	______
______	spinster
widower	______
headmaster	______
______	waitress
______	ladies
______	authoress
______	conductress

Group 4 Creatures

Masculine	**Feminine**
______	bitch
cockerel	______
bull	______
______	doe
colt	______
drake	______
stallion	______
______	vixen
gander	______
ram	______
______	sow
cob	______
lion	______
______	tigress

You will find the word you need in this list.

actress	**dog**	**mare**
aunt	**duck**	**mayoress**
author	**duke**	**mother**
bachelor	**ewe**	**nephew**
baron	**filly**	**pen**
boar	**fox**	**prince**
brother	**gentlemen**	**queen**
buck	**goose**	**tiger**
comedian	**headmistress**	**waiter**
conductor	**hen**	**widow**
cow	**lady**	**woman**
daughter	**lioness**	

Holiday postcards

Read the messages on each of these holiday postcards.

abroad	**caravan**	**coach tour**	**fishing**	**pony-trekking**	**seaside**
camping	**climbing**	**farmhouse**	**holiday camp**	**sailing**	

From this list, write in the space the type of holiday each person is having.

1

I am writing this on the pier. We made a super sand castle today, but daddy stood on it. Xx

2

I didn't think much of the food at first but we are getting used to it. The waiter calls Mum: "bella signora"

Stephe...
102 M...

3

Yesterday was the best day so far. The wind was just right and the yacht really sailed! and Jane looks really smart in her orange life-jacket.

Andrew Briggs
7. Woodhouse Sq.
Leeds 1.

4

My body aches and I feel a bit like a cowboy. I am riding Punch all this week. He is the best in the stable.

5

Dear Jack,
Lovely weather Nice and quiet, too Dad helped me set up my new rod. We are going for Salmon tomorrow.

Mrs ...
42 T...
BIRM...

6

The new tow bar is working well and we have had no difficulty on hills

John Long
Fairway Grove
Manchester 6

7

Dear Auntie Mabel
The chalets are very clean and we are having a good time. Uncle Ted has entered the talent competition tomorrow night - more of his jokes.

8

This is a view from the top which we reached yesterday. We had to use the ropes coming down.

Jam...
42 N...
Bri...

9

Dear All,
Sally was most surprised when a cow stuck its head in the tent.

Mr & Mrs O'Brien
35 Shepton Rd.
Larne
N. Ireland

10

Dear Penelope,
Marvellous food, nearly all home grown. Pork, eggs, vegetables & milk. Haymaking makes you hungry - and tired. Love Bertha.

Mr & Mrs P Ross
97 Walton Road,
Dundee
Tayside.

11

Our seats are near the front, just behind the driver. There are some other children travelling with their parents.

Peter Evans
Holly Cottage,
Newport.
Gwent.

Hand and foot

A number of words begin with **hand** or **foot**.

A Complete each of these sentences with a word beginning with **hand**. (The first one is done for you.)

1. Aunt Evelyn is clever at needlework. Her sweater is *handknitted*.
2. The monkey had grabbed a ______________ of nuts from the bag.
3. Sometimes a ______________ has an adjustable strap.
4. Every new car should have a ______________ giving engine details.
5. The prisoner was so violent that the policeman had to use ______________.
6. A ______________, thrown into the room, caused a massive explosion.
7. They settled their quarrel with a ______________.
8. Please fill in the form in your best ______________.

B From the clues, write a word beginning with **foot** for each of these.

1. kick it ______________
2. in front of the stage ______________
3. a note at the bottom of the page ______________
4. platform on a steam locomotive ______________
5. to hear this, is to know that someone is walking nearby ______________
6. walk across it ______________
7. a servant or attendant in uniform ______________
8. this is for walkers, not vehicles ______________
9. puts air into car tyres ______________
10. the name for boots, shoes, sandals and slippers ______________

C After each of these sentences, write the meaning of the phrase which has been underlined.

1. Be careful if you play cards with Uncle Will. He is <u>an old hand</u> at it.

   ______________.

2. To decide who is to be captain, we will have <u>a show of hands.</u>

   ______________.

3. Your father will have to <u>foot the bill</u> for this window.

   ______________.

4. When the coach broke down, the passengers had to finish their trip <u>on foot.</u>

   ______________.

5. Every time Tom Wilson opens his mouth, he <u>puts his foot in it!</u>

   ______________.

WARNING

By each of these warnings write two sentences.

The first sentence should tell where you are likely to see the warning.

The second sentence should describe what may happen if you ignore the warning.

Rhyming words

In each of these groups of words, **underline the one word** in the brackets which rhymes with the first word.

1	**seize**	(eyes, lazy, size, ease, price)
2	**height**	(hate, heat, weight, white, gate)
3	**rhyme**	(wine, line, fame, team, lime)
4	**maze**	(lace, raise, gauze, mass, mace)
5	**roll**	(tool, meal, gull, foal, rule)
6	**steer**	(stair, fear, stare, star, their)
7	**food**	(good, road, rude, rod, load)
8	**reign**	(pain, bean, scene, ruin, plan)
9	**police**	(plaice, place, please, crease, rice)
10	**nation**	(fashion, mission, station, ration, nature)
11	**whole**	(rule, hole, tool, whale, wool)
12	**friar**	(fair, four, fewer, fire, favour)
13	**world**	(furled, would, lowered, willed, word)
14	**laugh**	(leaf, waif, chaff, tiff, chafe)
15	**ruse**	(raise, rise, rush, raze, refuse)
16	**graph**	(gruff, grope, giraffe, grape, wrath)
17	**fault**	(felt, malt, taught, meat, hot)
18	**choose**	(chose, loose, news, posy, loss)
19	**disguise**	(stares, hiss, raise, nice, eyes)
20	**plight**	(polite, plate, pleat, plait, plot)
21	**plough**	(rough, cough, bough, dough, enough)
22	**steak**	(teak, take, seek, stark, strike)
23	**suite**	(suit, suet, sweet, swat, white)
24	**wonder**	(thunder, wander, ponder, winder, sender)
25	**wrist**	(worst, wrest, writes, whist, wrath)

Reading a pie chart

A Tom made this pie chart to show what he did on a **normal schoolday**.
He had to account for every one of the twenty-four hours from midnight to midnight.
Each small division stands for one hour. From the chart, answer these questions.

1 On what did Tom spend the largest part of the twenty-four hours?

____

2 How many hours did he spend on lessons?

____

3 He was longer at school than the time you have just written. What else was he doing there?

____

4 How many hours did he count for meals?

____

Which meal do you think took the most time?

____

5 Under the heading 'Various' he included hobbies and running errands.
What else might be included?

____

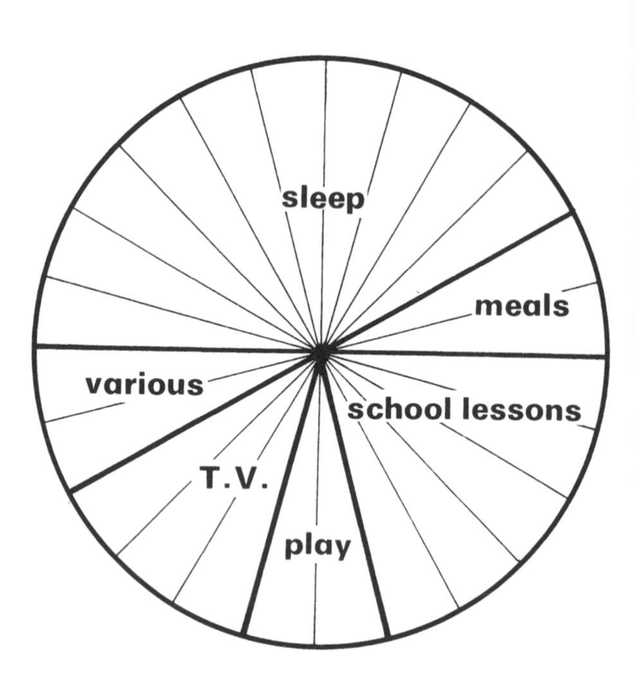

B In this circle make your own pie chart of how you spent last Saturday.
Each small division stands for one hour. You must account for all the twenty-four hours. Count up the hours for each of your activities.
Here are some possible headings.

sleep ________ meals ________

playing with friends ________

playing for a team ________

watching sport out-of-doors ________

watching T.V. ________ working ________

reading ________ visiting relatives ________

____

____

Show these as parts of the circle.
Label each part and colour each one differently.

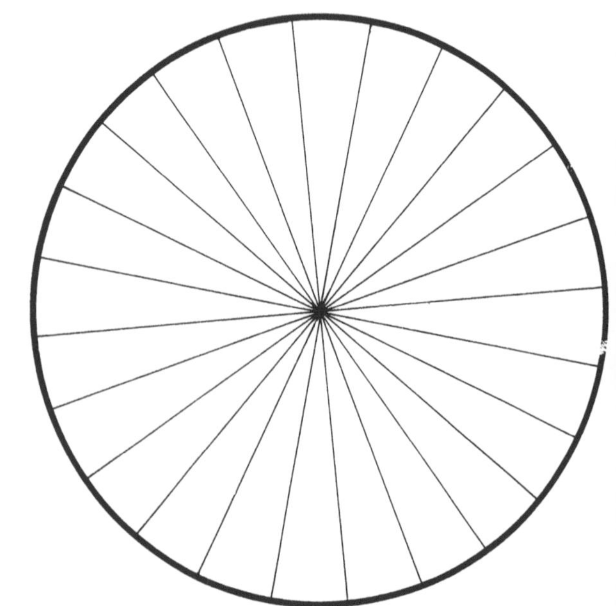

C Write sentences describing how your Saturday differs from Tom's school day.

____

____

____

Superstitions

A superstition is a belief that certain signs or happenings will bring **good luck** or **bad luck**.
By each picture, write what the superstition is about.

A

a black cat	a four-leaf clover	a ladder	a rabbit's paw
a chimney-sweep	Friday the 13th	a new moon	spilt salt
crossed fingers	a horseshoe	an open umbrella	white heather

Thur Fri Sat
5 6 7
12 13 14
19 20 21
26 27 28

SALT

B What do you think about these superstitions?

Schofield&Sims

the long-established educational publisher specialising in maths, literacy and science

Springboard is a series of nine graded activity books designed to help build the functional English skills required at school, at work and in other aspects of day-to-day life. Illustrations are used throughout to support the wide variety of activity types included. These range from the simplest word reading and letter formation exercises at the start of the series to complex writing tasks requiring considerable precision and attention to detail. **Springboard** provides many different contexts in which students are required to apply their knowledge, skills and understanding, giving them valuable practice and preparing them for full literacy.

Springboard 6 helps students to practise:

- Adverbs
- Past-tense verbs
- Meanings and definitions
- Masculine and feminine words.

The full range of titles in the series is as follows:

Springboard Introductory Book:	ISBN 978 07217 0883 6
Springboard 1:	ISBN 978 07217 0884 3
Springboard 2:	ISBN 978 07217 0885 0
Springboard 3:	ISBN 978 07217 0886 7
Springboard 4:	ISBN 978 07217 0887 4
Springboard 5:	ISBN 978 07217 0888 1
Springboard 6:	ISBN 978 07217 0889 8
Springboard 7:	ISBN 978 07217 0890 4
Springboard 8:	ISBN 978 07217 0891 1

For further information and to place your order visit www.schofieldandsims.co.uk or telephone 01484 607080

Schofield&Sims

Dogley Mill, Fenay Bridge, Huddersfield HD8 0NQ
Phone: 01484 607080 Facsimile: 01484 606815
E-mail: sales@schofieldandsims.co.uk

ISBN 978 07217 0889 8

£2.95
(Retail price)